THOMAS & FRIENDS™

THIS ANNUAL BELONGS TO:

 **AGE:**

THOMAS & FRIENDS™

Annual 2019

EGMONT
We bring stories to life

First published in Great Britain in 2018 by Egmont UK Limited
The Yellow Building, 1 Nicholas Road, London W11 4AN

Written by Laura Jackson
Designed by Martin Aggett and Elaine Wilkinson

 Thomas the Tank Engine & Friends™

CREATED BY BRITT ALLCROFT

ISBN 978 1 4052 9114 9
68290/1

Printed in EU

Egmont takes its responsibility to the planet and its inhabitants
very seriously. All the papers we use are from well-managed
forests run by responsible suppliers.

Stay safe online. Any website addresses listed in this book are
correct at the time of going to print. However, Egmont is are
that online content can be subject to change and websites
can contain content that is unsuitable for children. We advise
that all children are supervised when using the internet.

Adult supervision is recommended when glue,
paint, scissors and sharp points are in use.

CONTENTS

THE SODOR STEAM TEAM

Hello, Percy!

Percy is Thomas' best friend and can be found puffing all over Sodor delivering the mail.

Hello, James!

James likes to be a Really Splendid Engine and takes great care of his shiny, red paintwork. He hates getting dirty!

Hello, Nia!

Nia is from Kenya in Africa. She is always eager to help and she is one of the most adventurous of all the engines.

Point to your favourite engine.

FOLLOW THE TRACKS

Whoosh around the Island of Sodor and learn all about Thomas' busy day.

Say the answers out loud each time you land on a question.

Toot! Toot! Let's go!

First stop is the Steamworks.
How many steam engines can you see?

What is Thomas picking up from the farm?

Clickerty-clack!
Over the hill. What colour is Thomas' funnel?

Red signal!
How many sheep can you spot?

Last stop, the Quarry.
What has Thomas come to collect?

What a busy day!
Bye! Bye!

VERY IMPORTANT JOBS

The friends on Sodor are always busy.

Use a pencil and draw a line to match up the friend with their job.

a I tow broken-down vehicles and help out in engine rescues.

b I make sure the trains are doing what they are told!

Harold

Butch

c I travel on the roads and take people all over Sodor.

Toot! Toot!

Cranky

d I fly in the skies and help out in emergencies.

e I use my hook to lift heavy loads

Bertie

The Fat Controller

Answers on page 68.

FROSTY TRAIL

Emily is lost in the snow and is late for the Winter Party.

Guide her through the maze to her friends, collecting the candy canes along the way.

Watch out for the ice blocks.

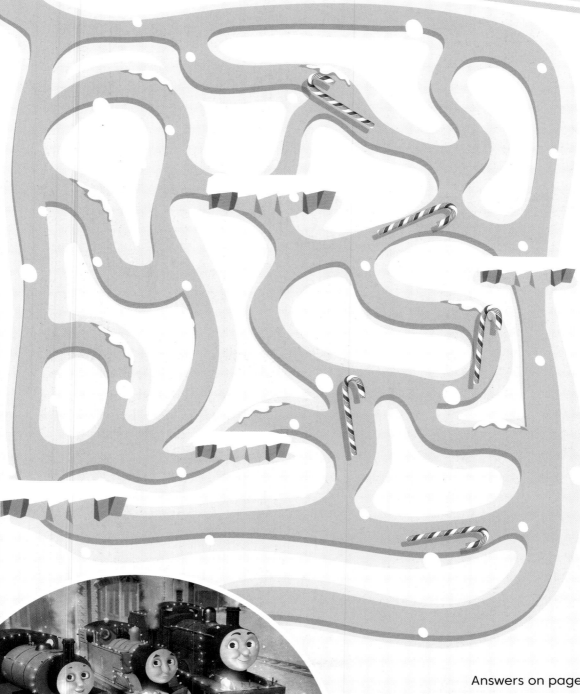

Answers on page 68.

SEARCH, SPOT AND SHOUT!

It's a busy day at Knapford Station.

Look at the picture to see what you can spot, then answer the questions.

Things to spot:

Plant

Clock

The Fat Controller

How many engines can you count?

1 **2** **3**

Point to the engine pulling red carriages

There are three ducklings hiding. Each time you find one, shout quack, quack!

quack!

quack!

THE FASTEST RED ENGINE ON SODOR ▶▶

James was a very fast engine. He loved being the fastest red engine on Sodor. But sometimes he went too fast.

"Screeeeeeeeeeeeeeeeeeeeeeechhhh!"

James' brakes skidded to a stop alongside Emily at Knapford Station.

"Stopping sharply like that is bad for your brakes," said Emily.

"I have to break hard sometimes, Emily," said James. "I am the fastest red engine on Sodor!"

Thomas pulled into the next platform.

"Fastest red engine, are you?" he said. "What about Rosie?"

"Rosie's not fast! She's not red either," chuffed James.

"She's red now," smiled Thomas, pulling away. "I just saw her."

"Like me, red? Splendid, red?" James called out. But Thomas had already left in a puff of steam.

Later, at the shunting yard James was coupled up to the Troublesome Trucks.

"I'm too Splendid to pull trucks!" groaned James, puffing out of the yard.

Just when he thought his day couldn't get any worse, he spotted a flash of red in the distance – Rosie!

James' brakes screeched to a slow stop as he pulled up alongside the newly painted engine.

"You really are red..." frowned James.

"Yes, what do you think?" asked Rosie, proudly.

There may be two red engines on Sodor now, but James was going to prove he was the fastest red engine!

"Want to race?" James asked Rosie.

Without waiting for an answer, James pumped his pistons and set off down the track.

James **whooshed** ahead. **Clickerty-clack, clickerty-clack.**

Rosie **chuffed** close behind. **Whirr, whirr, whirr, whirr.**

Soon the two red engines were side by side.

The signal turned red. Rosie slammed on her brakes and came to a quick stop. But James' brakes made another loud noise.

"Screeeeeeeeeeeeeeeeeeeeeeeeeeeeechhhh!"

He couldn't slow down and went right through the signal.

"James, STOP!"

called out Rosie. But James couldn't stop. He was racing further down the track straight towards Henry.

With one last pull on the brakes, James finally slowed down, just missing Henry's trucks.

James was shocked. What was wrong with his brakes?

"I don't think you should be racing,"

Rosie said, sternly. She took the Troublesome Trucks from James and ordered him to get checked over at the Steamworks.

James grumpily agreed. But, when he pulled up inside the Steamworks, his brakes didn't screech. He slowed to a smooth stop. So before anyone even knew he was there, James turned around and raced away.

"Ha, my brakes are fine!" said James, and he whooshed back down the Mainline. He soon forgot all about being careful and picked up speed.

"Wheee! Woo hoo!"

sang out James, flying up Gordon's Hill.

But then there was trouble. As James started to go down the hill, his brakes wouldn't work at all!

James couldn't stop and was going faster, faster, faster. James flew past Gordon.

He steamed through Knapford Station. All the while, going faster, faster, faster. With no way to stop and heading right for the Sheds, the Driver and Fireman jumped out of James' cab. James shut his eyes tight and...

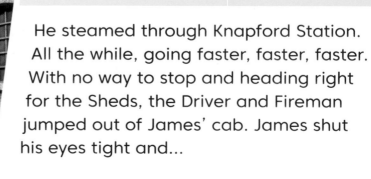

CRASH!

...James burst right through the back of the Sheds and brought the roof down! The Fat Controller was furious.

"Sir," said Rosie, pulling up to the Sheds. "James had problems with his brakes. He went to the Steamworks to have them fixed."

When The Fat Controller found out that James had left without getting his brakes checked he was even more cross!

"Sorry, Rosie," said James, quietly. "I should have known another red engine would give good advice."

"At least you proved one thing today," smiled Rosie. "You really were the fastest red engine on Sodor."

BIG WORLD ADVENTURES

When a racing car from Australia visits Sodor, he tells Thomas all about his travels. Now Thomas wants to travel the world and have an adventure, too.

START

1

2

Carlos

4

5

Squawk like a parrot.

7

8

10

11

Welcome to Kenya!

Nia

13

14

Welcome to Mexico!

Stomp like an elephant.

16

How to play:

- Each player places a counter or a button on START.
- On your turn, flip a coin. If it lands heads up, move forward two spaces. If it lands tails up, move forward one space.
- If you land on a friend or a flag you can move foward one extra space.
- The first one to reach Ace in Australia, wins!

FINISH

Ace

39

37

36

34

Bounce like a kangaroo.

33

32

Welcome to Australia!

Shane

30

29

27

26

Growl like a tiger.

Take a shortcut to avoid the tiger.

24

23

Welcome to China!

Yong Bao

21

20

Play this game with a friend and race across the globe to discover new places and new friends

18

All aboard!

MEET NIA

Nia is a colourful tank engine from Kenya in Africa. She loves being silly and laughing with her friends, and is always kind to everyone she meets.

Fun facts

- ✪ **Paintwork:** Orange with colourful patterns

- ✪ **Number:** 18

- ✪ **Nia loves...** to help her friends if they are in trouble

- ✪ **Nia is...** never afraid to tell people what she thinks

There are over sixty languages spoken in Kenya!

Wild Scribbles

There are lots of wild animals in Africa. Nia whizzes past elephants, zebras and lions on her travels.

What animals can you spot in this picture?

Use a pencil to trace over this elephant shape, and then give it some tusks, a tail and some big, floppy ears.

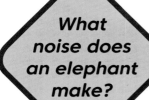

What noise does an elephant make?

ANIMAL MATCH

Peep! Peep!
Can you help Thomas to name the wild animals he meets.

a

elephant

b

c

giraffe

d

panda

parrot

What is the most exciting animal you have met?

Answers on page 68.

COLOURFUL NIA

Join the dots to make some steam!

Use your brightest crayons to colour Nia. Use the little picture to help you.

8
6 7 9 10
5 11
12
4 13
3 15 14
2 17 16
1 18

MEET YONG BAO

A colourful tender engine from China, Yong Bao is kind and brave. With a tiger painted on his tender, everyone admires him wherever he goes.

Put together, all of China's railways could loop around the world – twice!

Fun facts

⭐ **Paintwork:** red and green with yellow lining

⭐ **Yong Bao loves...** to pull passenger coaches all over China

⭐ **Yong Bao is...** a very brave engine who once stopped a huge rail accident from happening

A Really Useful Engine

Thomas is lost in the mountains. Using a pencil, carefully guide Yong Bao along the steep mountain track to rescue Thomas. If your pencil goes over the lines, start again.

RACE THROUGH CHINA

Fizzling fireboxes!

Yong Bao makes sparks fly when he whizzes through the Chinese mountains.

Toot! Toot!

These pictures look the same, but there are five differences in picture 2. Colour in a number each time you spot a difference.

1 **2** **3**
4 **5**

Answers on page 68.

MEET ACE

Ace is a rally car and lives in Australia. With a need for speed and danger, he finds adventure wherever he goes.

Fun facts

⭐ **Paintwork:** yellow with white stripes

⭐ **Number:** 43

⭐ **Ace loves...** to dream about where to visit next in the world

⭐ **Ace is...** afraid of wild animals and water. Maybe he's not as brave as he thinks!

Australia is home to sharks, crocodiles and snakes.

Vroom, Vroom!

Grab some crayons and design your very own rally car to race against Ace.

Give your car a name!

THOMAS AND THE DRAGON ▶▶

It was a bright, sunny day. Thomas the Tank Engine was chuffing along the Chinese railway with his friend, Yong Bao.

"You're so lucky to be here in China for the New Year," Yong Bao told Thomas.

Thomas noticed some people carrying pretty, red lanterns.

"Those are lanterns for the New Year party," said Yong Bao. "But do you know what the best part about New Year is...?"

Thomas chuffed as hard as he could to keep up with Yong Bao.

"... the DRAGON!"

"The what?!" Thomas called after him, but Yong Bao had disappeared into a tunnel in a puff of steam.

Moments later, Thomas caught up with Yong Bao at the coal hopper.

"What did you say was the best part of New Year?" asked Thomas. Thomas thought he had heard him say dragon. But surely there wouldn't be a dragon at the party?

"The dragon is the best part," replied Yong Bao. "Usually I take the dragon to the big square, but as you're a guest, I think you should have the honour!"

Thomas did not like the sound of this one little bit.

In fact, the more Thomas thought about the dragon, the more he began to worry.

"Don't dragons breathe out smoke?" he thought. **"And ... fire?!"**

When Yong Bao caught up with Thomas later in the day, Thomas was looking terrified.

"I really, really don't want to take the dragon to the party!" Thomas blurted out. "I'm sure it is a great honour but will you pull the dragon, Yong Bao?"

Yong Bao looked sad for a moment, but he agreed. "Okay, then you can take the lion."

"The lion?!" said Thomas, shocked.

The morning of the party, Thomas headed to Yong Bao's shed. He was coupled up with two coaches, An An and Lin Yong.

"Phew!" said Thomas, pulling off down the line. "I'm glad I am pulling you. I guess I don't have to take the lion after all."

"Oh yes you do, Thomas," sung An An.
"Oh yes you do, Thomas," sung Lin Yong.

Suddenly Thomas felt scared again.

He spent the rest of the day steaming from station to station, picking up passengers.

Clickerty-clack,
Clickerty-clack,

Thomas had a very busy day. But he couldn't stop worrying about lions and dragons.

Just as it was starting to get dark, Thomas pulled up alongside Yong Bao in the town square. It was filled with glowing lanterns.

"Wow, this party is amazing!" said Thomas, feeling happy there were no lions or dragons around. "I'm sorry I didn't bring the lion."

"But you did bring the lion, Thomas," said Yong Bao, smiling.

Two passengers got out of Thomas' carriage. They started pulling on two parts of a costume – a lion costume!

Thomas couldn't believe it. It wasn't a real lion after all!

"Look, here comes the dragon!" said Yong Bao.

Thomas gasped and closed his eyes tight. Then he heard a cheer. He opened one eye. And then the other...

"It's not a real dragon!" puffed Thomas.

The dragon was a beautiful, long costume, carried by people at the party.

"Of course not!" smiled Yong Bao. "What did you think?"

Thomas blushed and felt very silly.

"Maybe next time I feel scared, I will talk to someone. Then it might not be so scary after all!" Thomas thought to himself.

As the dragon was marched around the square, drums boomed and fireworks lit up the sky.

"That's what I was trying to tell you, Thomas," said Yong Bao. "The best thing about New Year is..."

"The dragon!"

smiled Thomas.

MEET CARLOS

Carlos may be small but he is a very strong engine. He lives in Mexico and is proud to be a good friend to everyone he meets.

Fun facts

⭐ **Paintwork:** Black with red lining

⭐ **Number:** 903

⭐ **Carlos loves...** to make people happy

⭐ **Carlos is...** strong. He was the winner of the strength competition when the very first Great Railway Show was held.

Football is the most popular sport in Mexico.

Funny Faces

Carlos is always smiling. Use a pencil to give Carlos a happy face, and then see how he looks with some other expressions.

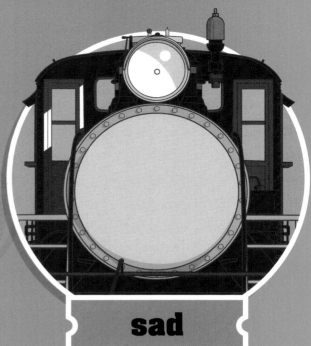

sad

happy

surprised

cross

ENGINE ART

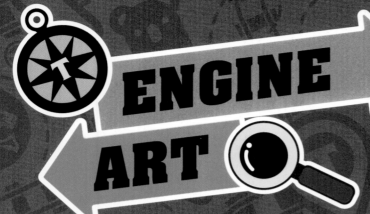

Some of Thomas' new friends have special designs on their paintwork.

Yong Bao has a tiger painted on his tender.

Nia has lots of colourful patterns on her engine.

Grab your crayons and draw some patterns on your very own engine – the brighter, the better!

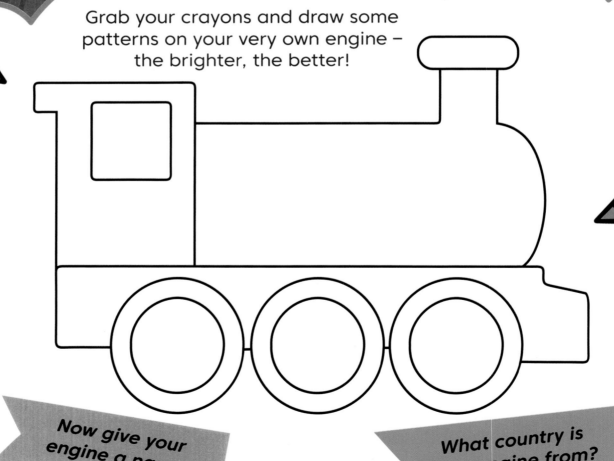

Now give your engine a name.

What country is your engine from?

DESERT DASH

Ace wants to race Thomas across the desert.

Ask a grown-up to set a timer and see how long it takes for you to follow Ace's path to the finish. Then do the same for Thomas' path.

FINISH

Who got the fastest time?

GUESS WHO?

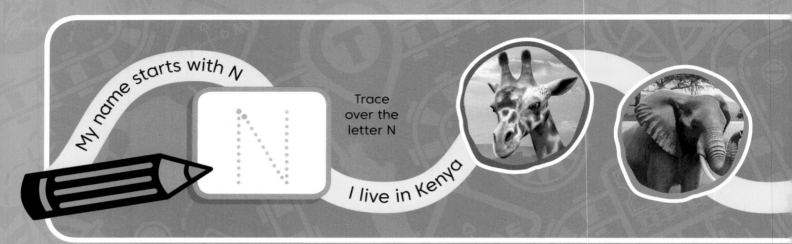

My name starts with N

Trace over the letter N

I live in Kenya

Trace over the letter A

My name starts with A

I live in Australia

My name starts with Y

Trace over the letter Y

I live in China

Follow the trails and solve the clues to discover which friends want to say hello.

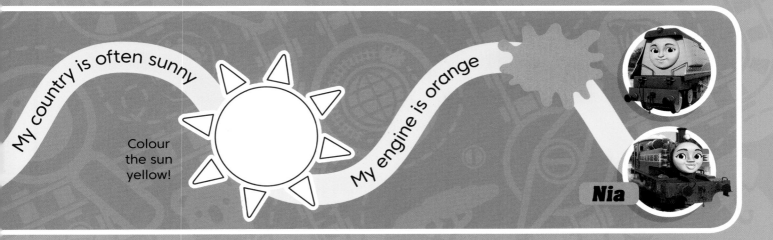

My country is often sunny

Colour the sun yellow!

My engine is orange

Nia

I race through deserts

Trace over the cacti, then colour them in

Ace

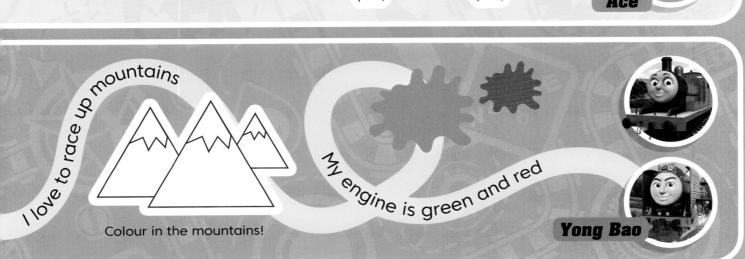

I love to race up mountains

Colour in the mountains!

My engine is green and red

Yong Bao

FLAGS OF THE WORLD

Thomas' new friends are very proud of their flags. Every country in the world has a flag, and each one is different.

These are just some of the world's flags. There are lots more!

This is my flag!

Australia

This is my flag!

China

This is my flag!

Mexico

Kenya

America

Germany

France

Britain

Russia

Now follow the instructions to make your very own flag bunting.

You will need:
- *scissors*
- *crayons or felt tips*
- *ribbon*
- *sticky tape*

How to make:
- Ask a grown-up to help you cut out the flags on the opposite page.
- On the blank flags, use your crayons or pens to design new flags. You can copy some of the flags on this page or create your own ideas.
- Use your sticky tape to stick the top of the flags along the ribbon, leaving a bit of space between each flag. Then you'll have your own **flags-of-the-world bunting** to hang in your room!

THOMAS & FRIENDS™

THOMAS

COUNT ALONG

Use the number line to count up some of the new and exciting things and friends Thomas has seen on his travels around the world.

1 2 3 4 5 6 7 8 9 10

1 2 3 4 5 6 7 8 9 10

1 2 3 4 5 6 7 8 9 10

1 2 3 4 5 6 7 8 9 10

Answers on page 68.

51

JOURNEY TO SODOR

It's time for Thomas to go back home to Sodor. Use your finger to guide him along the track, stopping at each friend to say goodbye.

Welcome home!

When you pass a friend, colour in a passport stamp at the bottom of the page.

Bye! Bye!

Ace

Bye! Bye!

Carlos

Bye! Bye!

Yong Bao

I visited Australia with Ace

I visited China with Yong Bao

I visited Mexico with Carlos

MEET REBECCA

Strong and speedy, this big tender engine is the new member of the Steam Team. Even though she gets into clumsy crashes and bashes, she travels everywhere with a smile!

Fun facts

✪ **Paintwork:** Yellow, red and orange with navy and white lining

✪ **Number:** 22

✪ **Rebecca loves...** to laugh with her friends

✪ **Rebecca is...** always going faster than she thinks!

Knapford Station is the biggest and busiest station on Sodor.

Guess with Rebecca

Answers on page 68.

Can you help Rebecca solve these puzzles?

1

2

a

Tick the **HAPPY** face.

b

Tick the **LONGEST** load.

1

2

c Draw a circle around the **BIGGEST** engine.

d Draw a circle around the engine with the **TALLEST** funnel.

Well done!
Now colour in your badge.

I guessed with Rebecca!

R

THE BIG FREEZE

1 One cold, snowy day The Fat Controller tells the engines that coal is running low.

2 The freezing weather means that coal deliveries can't get through.

3 Later that day, all engines are ordered back to the Sheds before their coal runs out.

4 Thomas has other ideas. He wants to drop his passengers off first.

5 But his coal runs out and he gets stuck in a siding.

6 Poor Thomas shivers all night outside in the icy winds.
"It's f-f-f-freezing!"

7 The next morning, the sun warms up Sodor. Diesel can finally deliver the coal.

8 Now all the engines are back on the go! **"Diesel, you're our hero!"** say Annie and Clarabel.

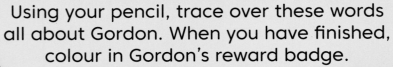

PENCIL READY

Well done!

Using your pencil, trace over these words all about Gordon. When you have finished, colour in Gordon's reward badge.

blue

train

fast

strong

Use your pencil to pile Gordon's flatbeds high with cargo.

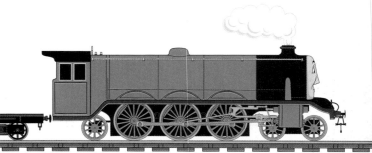

DANGER, DANGER!

Follow the tracks to find out which friend is racing to which emergency.

Percy

1

Thomas

2

Donald

3

a

Mooo! There's a cow on the line

b

Fizzling Fireboxes! Rex has come off the rails.

c

Brrrrr! Douglas is trapped in the snow

Answers on page 68.

MEMORY GAME

Look at this picture of Percy for 15 seconds,
then cover it up and see how much you can remember.

Answers on page 68.

1 What animal is stuck on Percy's buffer?

2 Is Lord Callan wearing trousers?

3 Does Percy look happy or worried?

4 Is it night or day?

UP CLOSE WITH THOMAS

Come and learn about all the different parts of Thomas the Tank Engine.

Steam from the top of the boiler is collected in the **dome**.

The **whistles** warn trains that Thomas is on his way. **Peep! Peep!**

The Driver and Fireman control the engine in the **cab**.

Steam comes out of the **funnel**. **Puff! Puff!**

Buffers to push trucks and carriages.

Water is heated in Thomas' **boiler**.

Wheels to go round and round and help Thomas move.

Coupling to pull trucks and carriages.

CONFUSED COACHES

Read the story about Gordon and Spencer. Listen to the words and join in when you see a picture!

Gordon   Spencer   platform   The Fat Controller   Fireworks

One snowy day at Knapford Station, rolled into

 two alongside 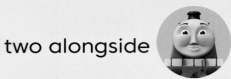. "If *you* were special, *you'd* be

leaving from one, like me," teased . So the next

day, when arrived to take the Duke of Boxford to Callen

Castle for New Year's Eve, he slid into one.

 was very cross when he had to pull into two!

The engines were so busy arguing, they didn't notice they had

been coupled up to the WRONG coaches. was pulling the

Duke of Boxford's carriages and was pulling the Express.

The engines raced each other down the mainline. But when

 got to his first stop, he was shocked to see and

Lord Boxford tumble out of the carriages.

 raced past, pulling 's coaches. " follow that engine!" shouted . But steamed on ahead.

The Express passengers were missing their stops! At last, and pulled into Callen Castle. When the angry passengers got out, couldn't believe his eyes!

"Sorry, sir," the engines said, quietly.

ordered  and to take the Express

passengers back to their stops. By midnight, the engines finally

pulled into Knapford Station. They were so tired, they didn't

care if they were on one or two. exploded

up in the sky. "I'm sorry I took your ," said .

"I'm sorry I teased you," said .

"Happy New Year!"

A REALLY USEFUL CHART

I listened to a friend.

Well done!

T

I worked as a team.

Well done!

T

I helped a friend when they were in trouble.

Well done!

T

Colour in a badge each time you do something kind or helpful.

I tidied up after myself.

I was kind and caring to animals.

I went to bed on time.

ANSWERS

Page 12

a. Butch
b. The Fat Controller
c. Bertie
d. Harold
e. Cranky

Page 13

Page 26

a. Giraffe
b. Parrot
c. Panda
d. Elephant

Pages 30-31

Page 51

7 pandas
5 engines
8 elephants
3 giraffes

Page 55

a. 2
b. 1
c.

d.

Page 59

1. b
2. c
3. a

GIVE THE GIFT OF A PERSONALISED BOOK
Perfect for every occasion

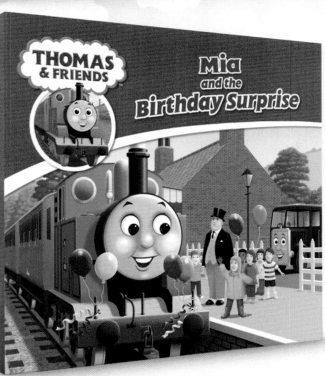

For our full range of books
visit **shop.egmont.co.uk**

EGMONT